When I Grow Up I Want To Be...®

a Veterinarian!

Sofia's Dream Comes True!

Wigu Publishing | Sun Valley, ID

Library of Congress Control Number: 2014914041

ISBN 978-1-939973-14-6

When I Grow Up I Want To Be... is a registered trademark of Wigu Publishing, LLC. The word Wigu and the Wigu logo are registered trademarks of Wigu Publishing, LLC. The words When I Grow Up... and Cuando Crezca Quiero Ser... are trademarks and/or registered trademarks of Wigu Publishing, LLC.

Wigu Publishing is a collaboration among talented and creative individuals working together to publish informative and fun books for our children. Our titles serve to introduce children to the people in their communities who serve others through their vocations. Wigu's books are unique in that they help our children to visualize the abundant opportunities that exist for them to be successful and to make a difference. Our goal is to inspire the great leaders and thinkers of tomorrow.

First edition, paperback, 2014

10 9 8 7 6 5 4 3 2 1

Quantity sales: Special discounts are available on quantity purchases by corporations, associations, promotional organizations, and others. For details, please contact the publisher at

Wigu Publishing

P.O. Box 1800

Sun Valley, ID 83353

inquiries@wigupublishing.com

Please visit our website at www.whenigrowupbooks.com for more information.

Proudly printed and bound in the United States of America.

"I am in favor of animal rights as well as human rights.
That is the way of a whole human being."
—Abraham Lincoln

"Our task must be to free ourselves...
by widening our circle of compassion to embrace all
living creatures and the whole of nature and its beauty."
—Albert Einstein

"With regard to animals, they not only have life but
feelings of pleasure and pain, too. We should treat their
lives with respect."
—His Holiness the Dalai Lama

"The greatness of a nation can be judged by the way its
animals are treated."
—Mahatma Gandhi

"Nature teaches beasts to know their friends."
—William Shakespeare

"The love for all living creatures is the most noble
attribute of man."
—Charles Darwin

"The best doctor in the world is a veterinarian. He can't
ask his patients what is the matter—he's got to just know."
—Will Rogers

The Veterinarian Oath

Being admitted to the profession of veterinary medicine, I solemnly

swear to use my scientific knowledge and skills for the benefit

of society through the protection of animal health and welfare,

the prevention and relief of animal suffering, the conservation

of animal resources, the promotion of public health, and the

advancement of medical knowledge.

I will practice my profession conscientiously, with dignity, and in

keeping with the principles of veterinary medical ethics.

I accept as a lifelong obligation the continual improvement of my

professional knowledge and competence.

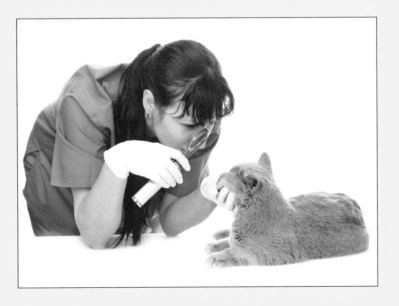

Sofia's greatest dream is

to have a pet all of her

own. One rainy night, an

unexpected visitor shows

up that just might make her

wish come true…

if only her mom would say,

"Yes!"

The answer was always "no."
And she always meant it.

Sofia wanted a pet. But whenever she asked her mom, the answer was always: "No. And I mean it, Sofia!"

No matter how many times or how many ways Sofia asked, the answer was still "no."

Sometimes Mom just said, "No." Sometimes she said, "Didn't I already tell you 'no'?" And sometimes it was, "¿Otra vez, Sofia?"

But it was always "no."

And she meant it.

But Sofia desperately wanted a pet, and no amount of "nos" could stop her from asking, or dreaming, about a pet of her own.

She thought about animals all the time—animals in jungles, in forests, in oceans, on mountains!

At school, she learned about people who traveled around the world to learn about animals. She spent hours looking at the animal posters in her room. She collected stuffed animals to share the top of her dresser with her soccer trophies and ceramic angel figurines.

Sofia loved animals. She wanted to care for every animal in the world. Her father said she got that part of her personality from her mother.

What she also got from her mother was a "no" whenever she asked for a pet of her own!

"Sofia, I know you want a pet, but you need to learn about the kind of animal you want. You need to know how to take care of a pet properly. It's a huge responsibility! Wanting a pet is not a good enough reason to get one," said Mom. "I don't think we are ready yet. We do not need a pet now. Maybe someday. We'll see."

For Sofia, "someday" did not hold much promise, until one night when something magically magical happened.

It rained.

Sofia watched the rain come down. Her father liked to say sometimes that it rained cats and dogs. *I know that's just an old saying, but I wish it were true. Maybe just one cat?* she thought.

Sofia watched from her upstairs bedroom as the cold night rain formed puddles in her backyard and streamed down her window. Then, through the rain, she thought she saw something scamper across the yard toward the back porch. A moment later, she was certain.

It was a cat.

The creature was a very rained-on, sorry-looking cat, but a cat for sure. To Sofia it looked exactly like the pet she always wanted!

Sofia flew down the stairs. When she opened the back door, the noise startled the cat. Sofia watched as the cat ran back into the darkness. Sofia was alone again, looking out into the lonely night.

Just then Mom called, "Sofia, why is the back door open? What are you doing?"

"There's a cat outside in the rain and cold," answered Sofia.

Her brother, Diego, came over and said, "So where did it go? Are you really sure you saw a cat, or are you just dreaming again?"

"I scared it away when I opened the door!" Sofia felt like crying.

"Maybe it will come back," Diego offered.

"No doubt a stray," said Mom, as she peered out through the kitchen window. "People should be more responsible about animals. There are too many unwanted animals running around."

"I can't believe any pet could be unwanted," said Sofia.

"It's sad, but true," said Mom.

Sofia waited and watched until bedtime. No matter how hard she looked, the cat did not return that night, even though it got colder and rained harder.

Lots of rain. But no cats or dogs, thought Sofia.

She whispered out to the night, "Where are you, kitty? Maybe if I wish real hard you will come back."

The next evening, from the backyard, Sofia heard a faint little cry, just barely a "meow."

I knew it. I knew it! I knew you'd come back! I won't scare you this time! I'm going to take care of you! Sofia promised, mostly to herself. She hurried to the kitchen. She put some dinner leftovers into the blue plastic bowl she used when she was little. Sofia then carefully placed the bowl on the porch, backed up a bit, and waited.

Slowly, cautiously, the cat approached the bowl, sniffed, and then ate hungrily. The cat looked up at Sofia between each bite. Each time it did, Sofia smiled at the cat. When it had finished its meal, it meowed, much louder than before.

"Shhhh!" said Sofia. "Someone will hear."

Just then, Mom appeared. She looked at the cat and watched as it scrambled back into the night. Then looking at the empty bowl, Mom said, "Let me guess. You fed her?"

"Yes," said Sofia. "It was hungry. But I didn't let it in!" Then it sunk in. "Her? Is it a girl cat?" asked Sofia. *That would be even better.*

"Possibly," said Mom. "Honey, I hope you didn't give her milk. That can make a cat sick. And she's not looking very well as it is."

"Really? Are you worried about the cat?" asked Sofia.

"I'm worried that if you feed a cat, it'll come back every night for more. We don't want that."

That's just what I want, thought Sofia.

The next night, it stopped raining. And sure enough, there was the cat, looking for food but not looking a whole lot better.

"What am I going to do with you?" Sofia asked the cat.

Diego came over and asked, "Are you going to feed it again? Mom's not going to like that idea."

Then Mom came to the back door. "Sofia, what am I going to do with you? And just look at that poor thing! It looks miserable."

"Sure does," said Diego.

Dad walked over and just nodded.

"Can I keep Samantha?" asked Sofia.

"Then I get a pet, too, right?" asked Diego.

"Wait a minute! One at a time! Who is Samantha? Don't tell me you have gone and given that cat a name. How do we even know it's a female?" asked Mom. She hid her face in her hands. Sofia couldn't tell if Mom was laughing, crying, angry, or all three.

"I just know she's a girl. May I please just feed her?" pleaded Sofia.

"Well, you might as well give the poor thing something to eat," said Mom. "But no more table scraps after tonight."

What is going to happen to Samantha if I can't feed her? Sofia worried.

"So does that mean no pets?" Diego asked.

"What I meant was no more *table scraps*," replied Mom. "If you are ever going to get a pet, you have to learn how to take care of it responsibly, and that starts with the proper food. We'll get some cat food for her. That will be better."

Sofia asked, "Will she come back tomorrow?"

Mom smiled. "You keep feeding that cat, and she's never going to leave." Mom crouched down beside Samantha and looked at her more closely.

"Never" would be wonderfully wonderful, thought Sofia.

"I don't know," Mom said. "There is something not quite right about this cat."

Dad looked at the cat and said, "If it doesn't look well, let's take it to our friend Dr. Helen. She's a vet."

An animal doctor is called a veterinarian, or vet. Some vets treat a variety of animals, while others treat only certain kinds. There are vets for animals in households, on farms and ranches, in zoos, and in the wild. They can help you pick the right pet and make sure you know how to properly care for it.

"I don't know," Mom said again.

"Well, we can't just let it stay sick and wet. If it's not healthy, we really should take it to the vet," said Dad.

"It stopped raining. It's dry," said Mom. But then she sighed. "Ok, fine."

"Let's go now, quick!" Diego yelped. "Before Mom changes her mind!"

Everyone laughed.

Dad took a cardboard box from the hall closet. He carefully lifted Samantha into the box, and the whole family drove to Dr. Helen's office. Samantha meowed and meowed.

"She's just scared because she's never been in a car before," said Sofia.

Diego asked, "How do you know? Maybe someone just drove her here and abandoned her?"

"I know," said Sofia.

In Dr. Helen's waiting room, Sofia studied a chart on the wall with all kinds of cats. She found one with a tail like Samantha's and another one with Samantha's ears—but not one exactly like Samantha. *Samantha is like no other cat in the world,* thought Sofia.

Dr. Helen came in, and Mom took the lead. "We want to give Samantha a checkup to make sure she's ok."

"Of course," said Dr. Helen. "Come into the examining room."

Sofia looked at all the posters and diagrams in the examining room. *Just like in my doctor's office except they are all about animals,* she thought.

"Do you think Samantha will be ok? Is she a girl cat?" asked Sofia.

"Well, let's find out. Is she a stray?"

"Not anymore," said Sofia. Dr. Helen smiled.

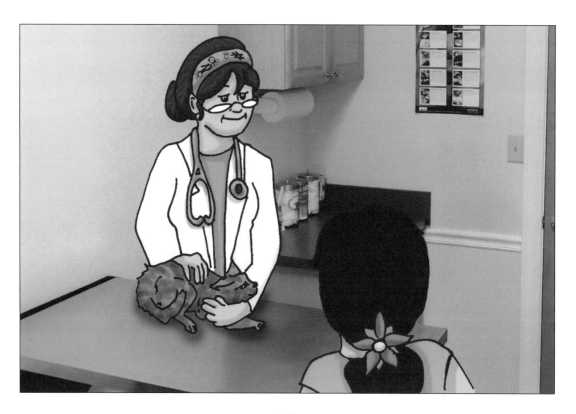

"Well, she's a female alright," said Dr. Helen.

Sofia thought, *I knew it!*

"First things first," said Dr. Helen. "See this instrument? It's a microchip scanner. Responsible cat and dog owners have tiny microchips put inside their pets so we can tell if they belong to anyone."

"What does it say?" asked Sofia, holding her breath.

"No chip. No registered owner," said Dr. Helen.

Sofia's heart soared. "That's because I'm the owner!" she said.

Dr. Helen put on her stethoscope and listened to Samantha's heart.

Diego asked, "Do you treat all kinds of animals?"

"Mainly small animals in this office. I leave the large animals to my husband, Dr. Karl. I don't have a big enough door for cows or horses," she joked.

Dr. Helen put Samantha on a small, flat scale and weighed her.

Sofia wondered, *Are animal checkups like mine? How do they weigh an elephant? What happens when a giraffe gets a sore throat? What about looking into a lion's mouth? Good luck with that!*

Many vets specialize in small, household animals. Dogs and cats are the most popular animals in homes. These companion animals are often considered part of the family. Animals that have learned to live alongside humans are called domesticated.

"Does Dr. Karl like farm animals because he was raised on a farm?" asked Sofia.

"Yes, he grew up on a farm in California with horses, mules, donkeys, and cows. But he likes all kinds of animals."

"Farmers have lots of animals," said Sofia.

Dr. Helen smiled. "It's an important job to make sure all animals are healthy because we share our planet with them. Animals provide us with protection, companionship, and some of the food we need to live. Take cows, for example. We want our cows to be healthy so our milk is safe for cheese, milk shakes, and ice cream. Ice cream made from the milk of a sick cow can make you sick."

Farm and ranch animal vets are considered large-animal vets (even though some of their animals are not that big). These vets keep domesticated livestock such as cattle, sheep, and horses healthy. They often travel long distances. They work in barns, in fields and meadows, and in all kinds of weather to treat their patients.

Sofia said, "I love baby horses. Ponies are so adorable."

"Yes, ponies are cute," said Dr. Helen. "So are baby horses. You know, of course, they are not the same thing."

"I know," said Sofia, but she was not actually sure.

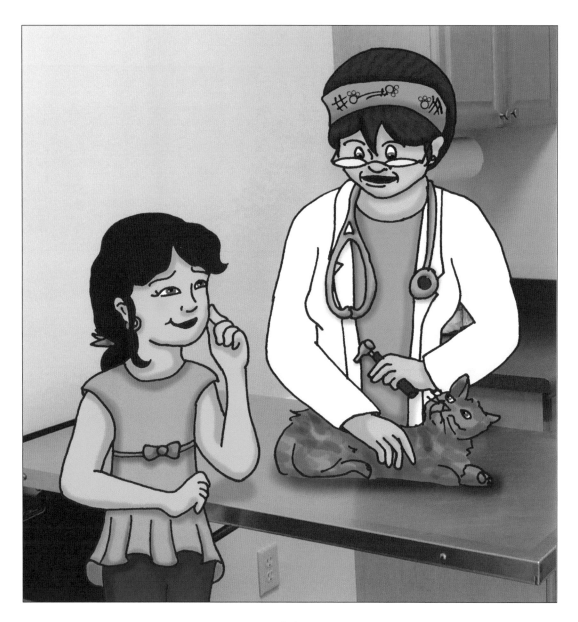

Veterinarians for horses and similar animals are called equine veterinarians. Horses are different in so many ways from other domesticated animals that they need special care. Vets receive training for the unique health needs of horses and other equine animals such as donkeys and zebras.

"Do large-animal vets take care of animals like elephants and hippos, too?" asked Diego.

"Yes! These days there are also vets who specialize in wild animals," explained Dr. Helen.

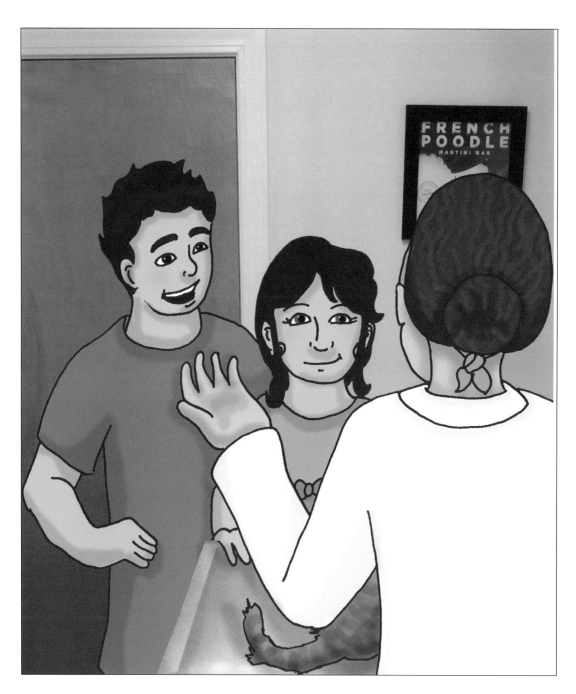

Veterinarians in wildlife medicine work with conservationists and zoologists to help all kinds of creatures in the wild, both on land and in the water. Wildlife vets also treat zoo animals. Sometimes their jobs include animal rescue. They help injured animals heal so they can be returned to their natural habitat. Wildlife vets also help care for and protect endangered species.

"I went to school with some vets who were being trained to treat marine animals, such as sea otters, dolphins, and whales," Dr. Helen continued. "They were often the students who grew up near waterways and oceans. Time and again they saw injured marine animals in distress and wanted to learn how they could help."

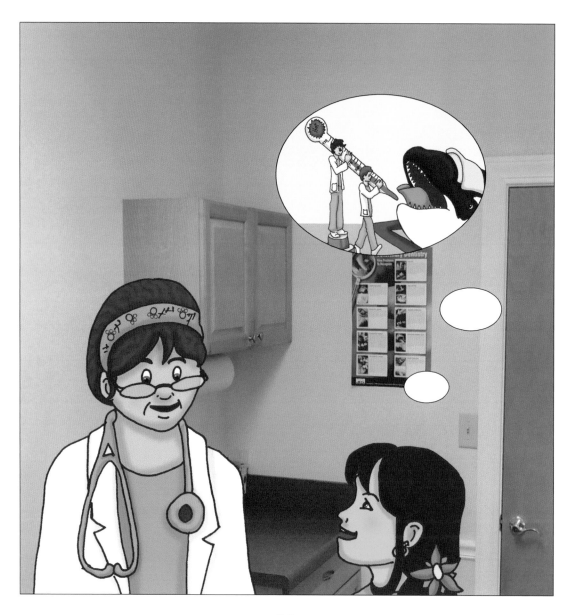

Marine animals, including mammals and birds, often suffer because of natural disasters, diseases, and problems caused by humans, such as oil spills. Animal rescue centers, shelters, and protected areas are an important part of keeping animals safe and healthy.

"There must be millions of animals to care for," said Sofia.

"More than you or anyone knows," said Dr. Helen. "Remember that most of the Earth is covered with water, and much of the planet has not even been explored yet. There are animals that no one has ever seen or may ever see."

There are an estimated 10 million different animal species on Earth. We don't know 90 percent of the species sharing this planet. Along with all the undiscovered animals, millions of new ones come into existence each year while others face extinction. If you become a veterinary scientist or explorer, you might discover a new animal…and you get to name it!

"It must be so awesome to have so many animals to take care of. How do you know how to treat each one?" asked Sofia.

"I went to vet school to learn all about many kinds of animals, inside and out, and how to care for them. We learned how animals behave and what treatments are best for each.

"You can tell your doctor where it hurts or if you have a stomachache or a sore throat. Animals can't. Vets have to diagnose, or figure out, with lots of other clues if an animal is healthy or if something is bothering it. So that's a big thing that makes our job different from a regular doctor's," said Dr. Helen.

"Wow. I never thought about it that way. You're like an animal detective!" said Diego.

Becoming a veterinarian takes a lot of study. The typical vet starts with a four-year college degree in a subject such as biology, chemistry, or animal science, just to get ready for vet medical school.

Vet school is just like medical school for your doctor, except vet students study animals. Vet students learn in classrooms and laboratories and also through extensive fieldwork. After four years of hard work, they become a Doctor of Veterinary Medicine (DVM).

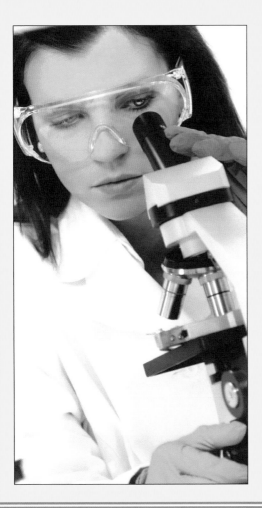
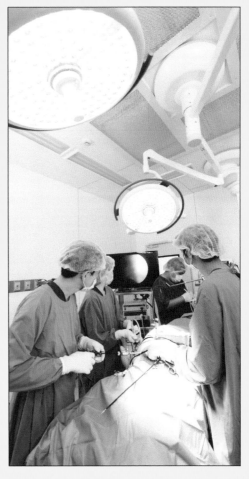

Dr. Helen used her stethoscope to listen to Samantha again, this time all over her back and belly. "Hmmm," she said and smiled. "You know it's great being a vet, making sure that pets are healthy and cared for properly. It's times like these that I really am glad I became a vet."

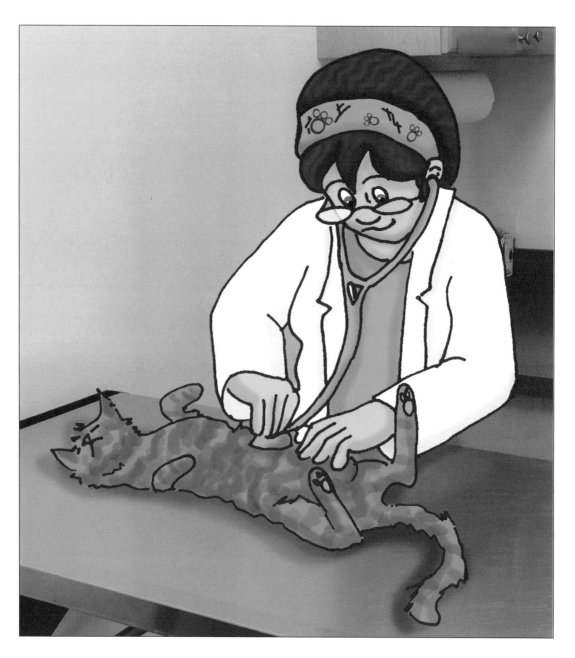

"Why did you become an animal doctor?" asked Sofia.

"I always loved animals and wanted to take care of as many as possible. I really enjoy helping animals," replied Dr. Helen.

"Me, too," said Sofia.

Still examining Samantha a bit more closely, Dr. Helen said, "I treat a lot of cats, not just strays, like yours. They are very popular pets."

Samantha is not a stray—not anymore, thought Sofia.

"They make good pets, and people often have more than just one," Dr. Helen continued.

Sofia and Diego grinned at each other.

Cats are the world's most popular pet. Cats are happy and comfortable living with people. They offer affection and companionship.

Throughout history, there have been cats of all sizes, shapes, and colors—from the tiny Munchkin to the giant prehistoric saber-toothed cat.

Cats became familiar and welcome additions to ancient households probably starting with the ancient Egyptians around 3,000 years ago. The cats kept rodents from getting into grain supplies. They also hunted dangerous snakes, including cobras. Cats were so important to early Egyptians that they were worshipped as gods.

"Do you take care of more cats than dogs?" asked Sofia, looking at a dog poster.

"A lot more dogs than cats, but I love them both the same. Each animal has a different personality and character. When you pick a pet for yourself, you should make sure it's a pet you can care for and live with for a long time. The owner and the pet must be a good match."

"That's Samantha and me," said Sofia. "We're a perfect match!"

Dogs may have been humans' first animal companions, beginning around 33,000 years ago. Scientists believe that all dogs evolved from the gray wolf millions of years ago.

Early humans discovered that dogs were helpful for hunting because dogs have keen senses of vision, hearing, and smell. Dogs also offered early humans protection and companionship, just as they do today.

Dr. Helen kept examining Samantha carefully. "Your cat's bones feel ok. I don't think we need to X-ray her. You know, some animals don't have bones, and some have skeletons on the outside, like armor."

"Outside like a snail?" asked Sofia. "Or no bones like a jellyfish?"

"Exactly," said Dr. Helen.

Dr. Helen then looked into Samantha's mouth and said, "Her teeth look good."

That got Sofia asking, "Are there animal dentists, too?"

"Yes. There are vet specialists for almost all parts of the animals, including teeth. Household pets need regular dental care just like you and I do."

"How do you clean a wild animal's teeth, like a lion or a tiger?" asked Diego.

"Carefully," said Dr. Helen, laughing at her own joke. "Even animals that don't have any teeth can still bite."

Sofia thought about that and said, "Right. Birds don't have teeth, do they?"

"Not that I am aware of," said Dr. Helen.

Birds can make friendly companions, too. Many birds, especially flock birds, thrive on good care and attention.

The word "avian" means bird or bird-like. Vets who care for birds are called avian veterinarians.

There are also veterinarians who learn how to treat exotic animals such as snakes, ferrets, hamsters, fish, and even tarantulas!

"When I grow up, I'm going to be a vet. I can't wait to take care of lots of animals," said Sofia.

"You may not have to wait very long," said Dr. Helen. "Samantha is not sick at all. Your cat is about to become a mother. She's going to have kittens."

"What?" exclaimed Sofia. "Really? Kittens? When?"

"Very soon. She's in labor right now," said Dr. Helen. "She'll have her litter here, where we can keep an eye on them."

Sofia could not believe her eyes when, minutes later, four little kittens came into the world. Each one was cuter than the next, all still with their eyes shut.

"I think four just about does it," said Dr. Helen.

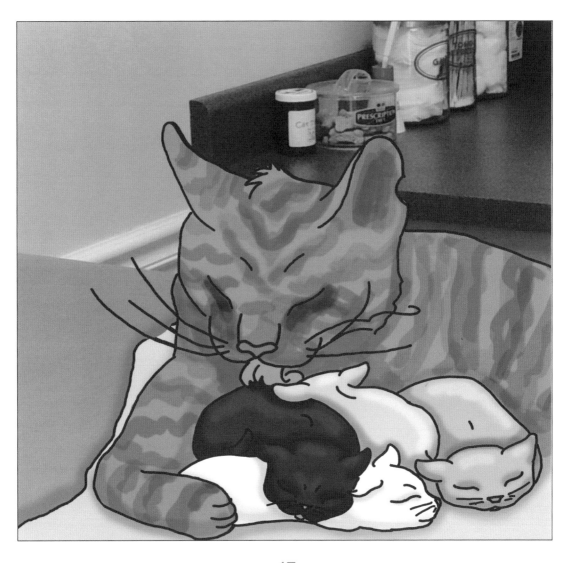

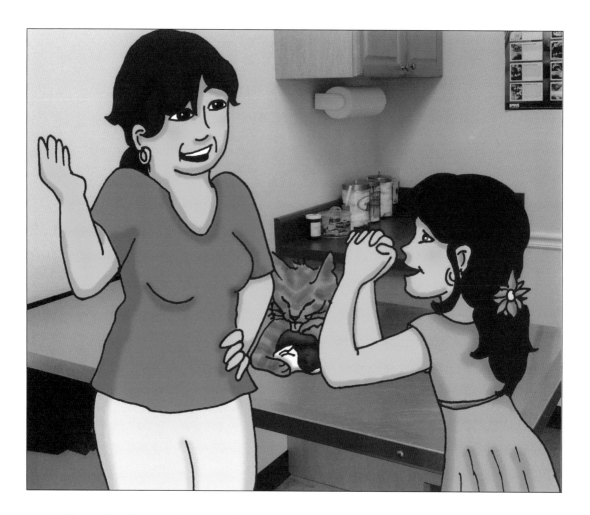

"Can I please keep Samantha now? Please, please, please?" asked Sofia.

Mom smiled and shrugged. She looked at Dad and said, "Well, I guess Samantha's yours now, Sofia. I think she's been yours since she showed up in our backyard. I know you will be good to her, and she will be good for you."

"I think Dr. Helen can give you some ideas about how to properly take care of her, too," said Dad.

"I'd be happy to," said Dr. Helen. "That's an important part of my job."

"Thank you so much, Mom," said Sofia. "Can I really keep Samantha, and maybe one kitten?"

"If Sofia gets two cats, I get to keep one, too, right?" asked Diego.

"¿Por qué no? I don't see where we have much choice here," said Dad. He laughed while Mom nodded her head. Diego immediately picked out the kitten he wanted.

"That's a male," said Dr. Helen.

"Now I've got to think of a name!" Diego exclaimed. "What about Sam?"

"What about 'Copycat'?!" said Sofia.

Everyone laughed, even Dr. Helen.

"Thank you, thank you so much!" said Sofia again to her mother, father, and Dr. Helen. "Isn't Samantha wonderful?

"When I grow up I want to be a veterinarian for sure," said Sofia. "I want to learn all about animals and have all kinds of animals to care for and love. Isn't that awesomely awesome, Mom?"

Sofia's mother said, "Yes."

And she really meant it.

What will help make me a great veterinarian?

I love animals.

Veterinarians are dedicated to protecting the health and well-being of animals. Veterinarians are animal lovers and understand the value of animals in our families and society.

I'm a good student.

A person interested in veterinary medicine should have a love of learning and good observation skills. A strong interest in biological sciences is also important.

I know how to listen to and help people.

Veterinarians must communicate with a variety of people. Compassion is essential for success, especially for veterinarians working with pet owners, who form strong emotional bonds with their animals.

I am a good leader.

Veterinarians often manage employees and businesses. Good leadership skills contribute to greater success in these work environments.

Be a Responsible Pet Owner:

Commit
- Think carefully before selecting a pet.
- Select a pet that best fits your home and lifestyle.
- Keep only the type and number of pets for which you can provide appropriate food, water, shelter, health care, and companionship.
- Commit to the relationship for the life of your pet.
- Provide appropriate exercise and mental stimulation.
- Properly socialize and train your pet.

Invest
- Understand that pet ownership requires an investment of time and money.
- Make sure your pet receives preventive health care, as well as care for any illnesses or injuries.
- Budget for potential emergencies.

Obey
- Clean up after your pet.
- Obey all local laws, including licensing, leash requirements, and noise control.
- Don't allow your pet to stray or become feral.

Identify
- Make sure your pet is properly identified with tags or microchips, and keep its registration current.

Limit
- Don't contribute to our nation's pet overpopulation problem. Have your pet spayed or neutered.

Prepare
- Prepare for an emergency or disaster by including an evacuation kit for your pet.
- Have a plan in place if you can no longer care for your pet.

When I Grow Up I Want To Be...®

a Veterinarian!

Sofia wants to care for all the animals in the world. But Mom does not think Sofia is ready for the responsibility of even one pet. Ready or not, when a hungry and sick-looking cat appears at the family's back doorstep, Sofia takes action. When Sofia is found feeding the cat, Mom gives in and agrees that a trip to the vet will tell them if the cat is healthy and not someone's lost pet. As the veterinarian introduces Sofia and readers to the important and wide-ranging work of animal doctors, Sofia learns how she might help all kinds of animals, including a little stray cat!

Reviews

"This book brought back memories of my own childhood. If your child ever says, 'I want to be a veterinarian,' this book is the place to start them on that road."—Peter Weinstein, DVM, MBA, Executive Director, Southern California Veterinary Medical Association

"This book is an incredibly impressive overview of all the career possibilities in veterinary medicine. The story is enjoyable and educational. I hope that it inspires a new generation to take care of the world's animals."—Blythe Wheaton, Cofounder and Executive Director, The Pet Rescue Center

"If your child loves animals like I do, this is a must-read!"—Silvia M. Colladay, DVM/CVA

"When I Grow Up I Want To Be...a Veterinarian! is an enlightening story about the ethical care of animals that the whole family will enjoy."—Candace Crespi, Oceanic Preservation Society

"Who doesn't want to be a veterinarian? I knew that I wanted to be a vet at age eight. This book would have been the one I read over and over!"—Karl E. Jandrey, DVM/MAS/DACVECC, Associate Professor of Clinical Small Animal Emergency and Critical Care Director, University of California, Davis

Wigu Publishing | Sun Valley, ID
www.whenigrowupbooks.com

Printed in Great
Britain
by Amazon